J

12,925

636
S

Schmidt, Karl Patterson

Friendly animals; illus. by Percy Reeves. Sponsored by the National Wildlife Federation.   Donohue ᶜ1947

64p   illus

Explanations of the origin and development of many of our domestic animals including the cat, dog, cow, sheep, goat, horse, donkey and hog.

1 Domestic animals 2 Pets   I Title

636

THE WOLF

FROM THE CALL OF THE WILD TO THE LOVE OF HOME

THE COLLIE DOG

FRIENDLY ANIMALS

By

KARL PATTERSON SCHMIDT

FIELD MUSEUM OF NATURAL HISTORY

Illustrated by

PERCY REEVES

SPONSORED BY THE NATIONAL WILDLIFE FEDERATION
WASHINGTON, D.C.

M. A. DONOHUE & COMPANY

CHICAGO   NEW YORK

12,925

CONTENTS

COLORED ILLUSTRATIONS

To My Late Brother

FRANKLIN JAMES WHITE SCHMIDT

IN MEMORY OF OUR LONG YEARS TOGETHER

ON THE FARM

.·.

*Readers who wish to study the origin of domestic animals
more extensively will find much of interest in works by
Richard Lydekker, "The Ox and its Kindred," "The
Sheep and its Cousins," and "The Horse and
his Relatives." Most of the studies on this subject have been published in German. A good
summary of modern views is found in
"Brehms Tierleben." The author is especially grateful for advice and criticism
to his colleague, Colin C. Sanborn.*

CHAPTER ONE

Introduction

MAN'S progress toward civilization is familiar to us in its main out-lines. Races of mankind who gain their living principally by hunting or fishing are the most primitive types. Such peoples represent the stage in which they are referred to as savages, and they are only too likely to include each other in their hunting. Sometimes they actually eat other human be-ings, and we look upon them with horror as cannibals. Sometimes they hunt each other in a game of war, or to extend their hunting grounds. In any case, we think of such savages as standing at the opposite end of the scale from our modern civilization. There are still peoples in the world who represent this primitive stage, like the more remote tribes of Indians in

South America, the black peoples of New Guinea, and the pigmies of the African forest. They use stone or wooden tools, and these tools are primarily the tools of the hunter—spears and arrows.

What would you think of as the first step toward civilization to be seen in even the most primitive tribes of men? I think it lies in the domestication of plants and animals. Savage hunters everywhere in the world have dogs to help in their hunting and to help guard their houses or tents at night. In some tribes the dogs are only tolerated; but among others there is an obvious fondness for animals which shows plainly what has been the first step toward permanent domestication of some of them. In many Indian villages in South America the traveller finds a veritable zoo of tamed birds and mammals. The American Indians had no domestic animals except the dog when the white man came; but when the white man's horses ran wild on the western plains, the Indians there soon learned how to tame them and how to ride, and altered their whole way of life in accordance with the acquisition of their second kind of domestic animal.

In the next stage toward civilized life we find the beginnings of agriculture among the hunters. Even the most primitive races supplement their diet of meat and fish with roots and fruits; and it was an easy step to learn to plant some of them in the neighbourhood of a camp, and to store roots and grains for the winter. In fact, the next domestication, after the acquisition of the almost universal dog, seems to have been the cultivation of corn by the American Indians, the raising of root crops like yams in the Old World, and, in some region not certainly known, the domestication of wheat.

On open plains the domestication of goats and sheep, and of cattle, horses, and camels, came directly after the hunting stage. Races of people who subsist mainly on the produce of their flocks and herds, and who move

8

about with them as they require new pastures, are said to be *pastoral* and are called *nomads*. The Mongolians represent such a race; so do the Arabs; and the life of the ancient Jews described in the first part of the Bible is exactly of this type.

Primitive man—when the agricultural stage had been reached by some and the pastoral by others—could begin the combination of these two ways of life. The work of clearing the land, planting and harvesting—at first all done by man himself—could then be combined with the raising of herds of cattle and sheep. On one hand, the stored grain afforded a food supply to keep the flocks alive over winter, or to fatten them; and on the other, the animals were soon pressed into service to help with the plowing, cultivating, and harvesting. This stage, however, is not very different from that of our own civilization less than a hundred years ago. The only addition modern man has been able to make to this combination of agriculture and stock raising is the invention of machinery. Even this machinery was at first always drawn or powered by horses or oxen. The change from the savage to the civilized way of life constitutes the main stream of human history. It is a fascinating story and in that story we must give our animal companions their proper credit.

Those of us who remember the last round of the barn at night—giving a handful of hay to one still-hungry cow, rearranging the straw for the favorite horse, taking perhaps a last look at some new-born addition to the farm family—are likely to think that these animals and their care and fellowship have been among the most important civilizing influences in the evolution of our society. Whether we come from farms ourselves and hold affectionate remembrance of our animal companions, or whether we are city-bred and know them at second hand, one of the most interesting things about the

9

story of our race must be the history of this companionship, and the origin of these fellow creatures. Sometimes that origin is fairly clear as in the house cat or domestic goat. Sometimes it goes back into the dim period of prehistoric man, as with the dog. In some cases, like that of the camel, our domestic breeds have no direct wild ancestors living. In other cases it is easy to point to a wild species from which the domestic form has sprung. Our first book about domestic animals will deal with the wild relatives of the most familiar types, and what is known of the history of their domestication.

CHAPTER TWO
The Dog and His Wild Ancestors

THE dog seems to have been the very first animal domesticated by any of the prehistoric tribes of man, and is still the only domestic animal found among the living races which remain in the savage stage. Dogs, furthermore, are by far the most widely known domestic animals even in the civilized nations. Animal companionship fills a deep-rooted want in man, and in the paved streets of cities with solid blocks of apartment houses, dogs are kept by a surprisingly large number of people. This is true both in the districts inhabited by the wealthy and in the tenements of the poor. The poor cannot afford the handsome or striking pure breeds, but their mongrels sometimes have a greater capacity for affection and often greater intelligence than the "aristocrats."

The closest wild relatives of the dog are the wolves and jackals. These are found in all parts of the world, and quite frequently the native races of dogs can be shown to resemble closely some native wolf or jackal. The dogs kept by the American Indians, for example, were scarcely at all different from the coyote, while the Eskimo dogs are more closely related to the arctic wolf. Our familiar races of dogs, however, are European so that the real question for us lies in the origin of the dogs of Europe and Asia.

The most outstanding trait of the dog is his loyalty and affection for the human beings with whom he lives. It is interesting to find these character-

istics developed to almost the same degree in tamed wolves and jackals. One of the peculiarities of dogs, which distinguishes them from their wild relatives, is the habit of barking. Wolf and jackal cubs brought up with a litter of puppies learn to bark quite as well as their foster brothers. The habit of hunting in packs, whether these are family parties as is usually the case with wolves or larger groups as in the jackals, has contributed something to their character. Perhaps the almost idyllic family life of the wolf, in which the father exhibits the same interest in the family that the mother does, sharing food with her while the cubs are nursing, and bearing his full share of the care and education of the cubs as they develop, may throw some light on the capacity for loyalty and love toward human associates which is so well known in dogs.

Dogs had already developed into a great variety of races by the time the first historical records were written. The greyhound especially appears frequently in sculptures of the ancient Egyptians, and has been traced back to about 3000 B.C. When we turn to the much earlier remains of the men of the Stone Age, the deposits left by them give us some definite information.

Great refuse heaps left by prehistoric man, known as "kitchen middens," along the coast of the Baltic Sea are composed of the shells of oysters and snails eaten by our savage ancestors. In them we find the older parts at the bottom, in which the stone implements are crude and rough, without any trace of the remains of dogs and, of course, without any of other domestic animals. At about the time when these early men learned to shape and polish their stone axes and spearheads—which shows the transition from the "Old Stone Age" to the "New Stone Age"—the first remains of dogs begin to appear in their kitchen refuse. These dogs were more like jackals than wolves; they appear to have been spread over all Europe and to have

Percy Reeves

THE WOLF IS THE ANCESTOR OF ALL THE DOGS

GREAT DANE

SHEPHERD

CHIHUAHUA

NO OTHER ANIMAL HAS DEVELOPED SUCH EXTREME VARIABILITY
IN SIZE, SHAPE, COAT AND COLOR AS IS FOUND IN THE DOMESTIC DOGS

persisted as a well-marked breed for thousands of years. At any rate, the dogs kept by the Lake Dwellers (about 6000 years B.C.) when the stone tools had been replaced with bronze, and iron was beginning to be used, were still very much like those first half-wild dogs that howled by night on the refuse heaps of the shell-fish eaters.

A larger kind of dog is also known from skulls and other bones found in the refuse deposits of the men of the New Stone Age, and this is as clearly derived from the wolf as the other is from the jackal. Many hunting dogs and the modern police dog or German shepherd seem to be mainly derived from this larger form. The crossing of these two types of dogs gave to early man the mixture from which he has since produced such a bewildering variety of domestic races.

No domestic animal has produced so great a number of breeds as the dog, and among these breeds the differences of body form, coat, and intelligence are likewise unparalleled. The wolf-like German shepherd or "police dog" and the dachshund, the poodle and the Pekinese, the great Dane and the terriers, the greyhound and the bloodhound, all have developed out of that ancient mixture of jackal and wolf under the influence of man. It is clear that many of the breeds, such as the tiny toy dogs, the longhaired poodles, and even the bulldogs, could not develop without the protection of civilization and could not possibly exist under natural conditions. It is equally clear that careful selection by human breeders is responsible for the existence of these diverse races, whether that selection has been merely fanciful or whether, as in the hunting dogs and shepherd dogs, it has been directed toward producing a race of the greatest possible efficiency and intelligence.

The first benefit of dogs to primitive man, when they were still only half-domesticated, was probably the outcry they made at the approach of

13

savage animals or strange men. This trait is preserved in many breeds which are maintained primarily as watch-dogs such as the jackal-like spitz, the mastiff and many of the terriers. Also the unmistakable evidence of broken skulls in the kitchen middens shows that, in time of need at least, dogs were eaten by savage tribes. This use of the dog for food persisted until modern times in the South Sea Islands, among the American Indians, and in some other parts of the world.

The use of dogs in the north for draft animals to pull sledges appears to be one of their earliest fields of service. The large, wolf-like Eskimo dogs seem to be extraordinarily efficient in this respect, requiring only a few frozen fish for a day's journey, and pulling loads of 100 pounds per dog thirty miles or more in a day. Dogs as draft animals appear occasionally throughout central Europe. Their use for pulling milk carts in Holland is familiar. In North America the Plains Indians often used their dogs as well as their horses in moving camp, making a miniature travois for the dog of the same type as the larger one for the horse.

The numerous breeds of dogs used exclusively for hunting, and the development of special breeds for different kinds of hunting and for special kinds of game, show that this use of the dog must also have been one of the earliest. Dogs easily recognizable as representing several distinct breeds are shown in early Egyptian sculptures, and among these the greyhound type is most prominent. Hunting dogs soon diverged into two classes—those hunting by sight like the greyhounds, the "*sight-hounds*"; and those in which the sense of smell became of primary importance, like the foxhound, the "*scent-hounds*."

The use of dogs in driving and guarding cattle and sheep has produced the various breeds of shepherd dogs, usually characterized by great intelligence.

14

Finally, the affectionate nature of dogs and some inner need in ourselves for animal companionship has led to the development of a great variety of lap dogs, used for no purpose but as pets. These may often be recognized readily as dwarf races of some larger useful breed, like the King Charles spaniel or the Italian greyhound.

In North Africa, southern Asia, and southeastern Europe, pariah dogs are to be found everywhere. These are genuinely wild dogs so far as any care on the part of man is concerned; but they are for the most part dependent on the presence of man for their food supply. They live upon the dead animals found in the fields or on roadsides, and enter the towns to eat the street refuse, sharing it with the swine. They enjoy a surprising degree of consideration even in Mohammedan communities in which dogs are practically outcasts, and may become extremely bold in snatching scraps of food. These pariah dogs are very jackal-like in appearance, and their scavenging habits are extraordinarily similar to those of the various wild jackals, which are camp-followers to the larger beasts of prey like the lion and the tiger, instead of to man. These pariahs evidently cross with wild jackals, for in India they resemble most closely the Indian red jackal; in Egypt they are like the Nubian jackal, and in South Africa there are similar half-wild dogs like the quite different black-backed jackal. It is generally believed that these widespread pariah dogs are descended from more completely domesticated ancestors and that they have become *feral*—that is, have run wild. We learn a great deal about the true characteristics of our domestic animals from these feral races.

A remarkable race of such feral dogs exists on the large island of Albemarle, in the Galapagos Islands. The dogs which have escaped from the small settlement at the south end of the island have acquired a considerable

15

uniformity of appearance, and live like wolves, hunting the native birds, digging up the eggs of the giant land turtles as well as those laid on the sand beaches by the sea-turtles, and hunting the similarly feral goats and cattle. They are as shy and difficult to approach as any wild creature, but young ones captured and brought up in association with man are again completely tamed.

Most distinct of all the feral races of dogs is the wild dog of Australia known as the dingo. The wild mammals of Australia, except for a few small rodents, belong to the primitive pouched mammals or to the still more primitive egg-laying mammals. They represent the first colonization of Australia with mammals, when Australia was connected with Asia, in an era so ancient that the pouched mammals were probably the most advanced type in existence. Since that time Australia has been separated from Asia and its animal life has evolved a great variety of types but without the competition of modern *carnivores* or flesh-eating animals, and of the hoofed animals. The dingo, a wholly modern member of the dog family, does not fit at all into the general picture of Australian life, any more than man himself. It is accordingly believed that the dingo was brought to Australia by the aborigines, and that its present independence of man is due to the fact that it could easily lead a self-reliant life in the midst of the inferior *marsupial* or pouched types which thronged the plains and forests of Australia before the advent of the white man. The dingo is strikingly like the pariah dogs of India, especially in the reddish color of its fur.

There seem to be at least three native wolves in the Americas from which the dogs of the American Indians have been derived. The North American Indians had dogs when the white man arrived, and these were very closely related to the coyote in appearance, size and habits. In Florida, the Semi-

EARLY MAN'S DOGS FIGHTING OVER THE KILL

THROUGHOUT THE AGES DOGS HAVE HELPED IN THE HUNT

nole dog seems to have been black like the local wolf. In northern South America and the West Indies, the very handsome crab-eating dog is still found as the domestic dog of the Indians. In southern South America, Azara's dog—a very fox-like creature—appears to be either the direct ancestor of the dog of the Pampas Indians or to have crossed with it so much that the relationship with any other wild dog is obscured.

Curiously enough, those wild members of the wolf family which are known as "wild dogs" are not as closely related to our dog as are the wolf and the jackal. The Asiatic wild dogs have one tooth less, and thus cannot be ancestors to our dogs. The fierce Cape hunting dogs of Africa, with their unusual coloration of black, white and yellow, are very dog-like in general appearance but have only four toes on both front and hind feet. The foxes have no part in the ancestry of the dog. They never cross with our domestic dogs, and the large-eared foxes of various types in Africa and Asia are still less dog-like. The American grey fox is likewise quite unrelated to the domestic dogs. Even the curious bush-dog of Brazil, one of the smallest members of the dog family, and one of the rarest and least-known, is said to be easily tamed.

CHAPTER THREE
The Forbears of the Cat

IT is not an accident that a child is likely to learn to read the words cat and dog at the very beginning of his school career, for these are sure to be words that he knows long before he goes to school. The contrast in their characters is our first lesson in animal psychology, and we think of cats as in some way the opposite of dogs. Cats are in fact almost as widespread in domestication as dogs, but the history of their spread through the world is a very different one.

The cats belong to a large family of animals, like the dogs, and some wild members of the cat tribe are found on every continent except Australia. Lions and leopards are found in Africa and India, tigers in most of Asia, and the jaguar and puma in the Americas. The short-tailed lynxes are found in North America, Europe, Asia, and Africa. Beside these there are great numbers of smaller kinds which are everywhere known as wild cats. Thus our cave man ancestors might have domesticated cats in the same way that they made pets and companions of dogs; but this is not at all the case, and no traces of domestic cats are to be found in prehistoric deposits. They are first heard of in Egypt, about 2000 B.C. It took centuries before they spread to Europe, and one of the curious things we learn about the ancient Greeks and Romans is that they kept ferrets, or some relative of the ferret, to keep down mice, and had no cats. House cats are not mentioned in

Percy Reeves

THE EUROPEAN WILD CAT MAY HAVE CROSSED WITH DOMESTIC CATS

AFTER THEY REACHED EUROPE

THE ANGORA IS ONE OF CATDOM'S ARISTOCRATS

Greek literature, but some of the early students of Greek writings translated the Greek word for "ferret" as "cat," and so confused the record of the arrival of the cat in Europe. Cats are not mentioned in the Bible either, so they evidently did not spread out of Egypt until quite a late period.

The rich soil of the Nile valley, suitable for raising wheat and other grains, was one of the principal reasons for the early appearance of civilization in this part of the world. When we look at models of the ancient Egyptian houses, we learn that large granaries were a usual feature in their courtyards, and we may be sure that there was already a plague of rats and mice. It is not surprising, therefore, that the small wild cat, native to North Africa, which is extraordinarily easy to tame at the present day, proved a welcome guest in these courtyards.

The ancient Egyptians even trained cats to help with hunting. Their paintings show that in addition to the long-tailed and black-footed wild cat, they employed the tamed swamp lynx to retrieve game, such as ducks, which they hunted from boats in the papyrus swamps.

The religious veneration of the cat in ancient Egypt is well known, and since their mummies of cats and their pictorial sculptures are well dated, we learn that this cult appeared about 2000 B.C., its special center being the city of Bubastis, where there were images of gods with the heads of cats, or in the form of cats. The death of a cat was a cause for mourning in the whole family, quite as if one of the human members had died; and the killing of cats, even by accident, was a grave offense. Mummies of cats are especially abundant, and may frequently be seen in museums. These mummified cats were so extremely numerous in the Bubastis cat cemetery that for some time they were regularly sold to be broken up for garden manure! This cat is plainly the first domestic cat, and it is not surprising to find that it is

19

directly derived from the Egyptian wild cat, which in turn is a race of the common small cat which inhabits nearly the whole of the African continent. The character which most plainly shows the relationship of our common cats to this African ancestor is the black undersides of the feet. The European wild cat has yellowish feet, with only a small black spot on each toe pad. The skull of the house cat is also more like that of the Egyptian wild cat than it is like that of the wild cat of Europe. The fact that the wild cat of northeastern Africa is easily domesticated also shows that it is the principal ancestor of our house cat, for even kittens of the European wild cat are difficult to tame. Meanwhile, historical records prove the same thing, namely that our house cats entered Europe from Egypt.

The time of the arrival of the Egyptian house cat in Europe has been set by scholars as probably about the beginning of the Christian era. Even as late as the fourth century A.D., cats were kept less frequently in Greece and Rome than ferrets. At this time the rise and spread of the great orders of monks and nuns played a part in spreading house cats from Egypt and Asia Minor through Europe, and they gradually became abundant. They seem to have spread eastward through Arabia, Persia, and India to China, where they are first reported in the sixth century B.C. They are not mentioned in the ancient writings of India.

It is possible that a few cats were brought to England by the Romans, but no trace of them remained after their departure, and we find no mention of them in English history or literature until the year 950, when laws were enacted in Wales to protect cats and to reimburse their owners if one was killed. The penalty for killing a cat was the payment of a heap of wheat which would completely cover the dead animal when it was hung up by the tail, with its nose touching the ground. Another valuation in the same

century made the killer of a cat forfeit a ewe and a lamb. It was not until the fifteenth and sixteenth centuries that cats became abundant throughout Europe. The story of the fortune made by Dick Whittington by selling a cat in West Africa is probably not true; but it no doubt grew out of the memory of the time when a single cat was worth two sheep.

It was thought for a long time that the European wild cat was the ancestor of the house cat. It is of about the same size, and its striped pattern is occasionally well shown in the tame form. It is likely that the domestic cats, which frequently enough run wild and become "feral," have crossed with this relative; but, their principal ancestry must be sought elsewhere, as we have shown. In spite of the fact that there is a good deal of color variation in our common domestic cats, there is nothing to compare with the hundreds of well-defined breeds of dogs. The Persian cats (or Angoras), and the Siamese cats, which are distinct breeds, will be mentioned further on. In the house cat we are familiar with a pure bluish gray type, the Maltese; a brown type with darker brown stripes on the sides, the "tortoise shell"; a black type, usually with a white spot under the chin; and various mixtures and even parti-colored specimens. This variability is one of the characteristics of domestication, and these types could no doubt be bred into pure races, if it were not for the fact that cats live an independent life of their own, and often run completely wild.

The fact is that the cat is very much more self-reliant than the dog, and less subject to man's control. The history of the domestication of the cat in one of Kipling's Just-So Stories, "The Cat that Walked by Himself," does not pretend to be true. But it is a very good story, and the fundamental truth about the independent spirit of the cat is finely set forth in it. From the first the dog seems to have been man's servant, while the cat remains

One cat equals two sheep

even to the present day a guest in his house. It is surprising how readily cats take to a completely wild way of life. Even in winter in northern Wisconsin, if a farm boy sets out some traps to make a little pocket money from furs, he is sure to catch some of these feral house cats.

The Manx cat is a fairly well-known and fairly well-defined race of the domestic cat found on the Isle of Man, in the Irish Sea. These cats have somewhat longer hind legs and a very short tail. There seems to be no doubt that this is a freak which may appear in the common house cat, and one which breeds true if some selection is practiced. Such cats are by no means confined to the Isle of Man, for they are known in Dorsetshire in England, and cats which exhibit various degrees of shortening of the tail are known from Java and Japan.

The long-haired Persian or Angora cats are handsome and distinguished looking creatures. They may be either yellow, white, or bluish gray, and have flesh-colored feet. They appear to be more intelligent than ordinary cats, and are sometimes much less affectionate in their behavior, especially toward strangers. Various authors have thought that the beautiful Manul cat of Central Asia, which has long hair, might be the ancestor of the Angora cats. It is perhaps possible that some crosses of the wild Manul cat with the typical house cat have taken place, just as we suppose that our house cat has crossed more or less with the northern wild cat of Europe. Long hair, however, is not uncommon in domestic animals, and this character may have arisen under domestication by selection. In any case, the Angora cats really appear to have come from Asia Minor, as their name indicates, and from the neighboring Persia. In spite of the fact that its long hair seems to mark the Angora cat as a more pampered race, they are wonderful mousers and ratters.

DOMESTIC CATS ARE DIRECTLY DESCENDED

FROM THE EGYPTIAN WILD CAT

OUR SERENE TABBY WITH HER AGILE OFFSPRING

The most distinct of all the house cats is the Siamese cat, which is short-tailed, with Isabella-colored fur, blackish on the face and ears, and with black feet and tail. It is quite likely that this is derived from a very different wild species, but it is still uncertain what that species may be. Originally, pure-bred Siamese cats were to be obtained only from the palace of the king of Siam. These cats have a curious resemblance to albinos, for the kittens are pure white, with pink eyes. They darken with age, however, and the eyes become bluish. They are intelligent and affectionate in a degree unusual in ordinary cats, and quite deserve to be called, as they often are, the "Royal Siamese."

CHAPTER FOUR

The Origin of Domestic Cattle

CATTLE are by far the most important of all the animals domesticated by man, and next to the dog, clearly the most ancient. It is curious that there is no generally current word for domestic cattle in English. Bull, cow, ox, steer, calf, heifer, etc., are all applied to the separate sexes, to a special class, or to the young animals, while the word cattle, which is plural, really may include other domestic animals as well. "Cattle" seems to be the same word (in its origin) as chattel, which means simply "possession." This is a very natural meaning, since in ancient times wealth was reckoned by the number of cattle owned, as, indeed, it still is among primitive peoples in Africa and Asia. That this was the original meaning of wealth among our own ancestors is well shown by the fact that the earliest known coins bear an ox head; and equally by our word "pecuniary," meaning wealth in money, which comes from the Latin word for cattle, pecus.

It is interesting to find that cattle were domesticated from earliest times both in Egypt and in the Syrian region. The record of domestic cattle in Egypt goes back at least to 3500 B.C. The life of the ancient Jews, before the captivity in Egypt, was that of a typical pastoral people, living in tents, and depending entirely on their flocks and herds for food and clothing. It is believed that the whole desert region of Mesopotamia and parts at least of Arabia had a climate with more rainfall in the prehistoric, and even the

early part of the historic period, so that what is now barren desert was grassland in those ancient times. The Bible is full of references to domestic cattle, which continued to be of primary importance in Palestine. After the pastoral people had adopted a more settled life, and a city-bred civilization had developed, we read of the milk cows, of oxen used for pulling carts and plows, and of the stall-fed ox and the fatted calf.

In contrast with the very great importance of cattle in western Asia, and Europe, in both ancient and modern times, it is strange to find that cattle were never very highly valued in China, Japan, or Korea. The people of these oriental countries do not use milk and its products, butter and cheese, as we do. In India, on the other hand, cattle play the same important rôle that they do in our western civilization, and still keep a great religious importance, which they have lost with us. This may remind us that the Indians of India are related in race to the white European peoples, and not to the Malays and Chinese.

A mighty wild ox, the "aurochs," was hunted by our forefathers in Europe. It roamed the forests of central Europe down to historic times, and this wild species was quite certainly the true ancestor of the west Asiatic and European breeds of cattle. This remarkable creature became extinct about the year 1627. We hear of it in history first from a graphic note by Julius Caesar, in the journal of his war with the German tribes beyond the Rhine, about the year 65 B.C. His record, translated freely from the Latin, is as follows: "There is a third kind of these animals which are called uri. In size these are but little inferior to elephants, although in appearance, color, and form, they are bulls. Their strength and their speed are great. They spare neither men nor beasts when they see them. The hunters are most careful to kill those which they take in pitfalls, while the young men exercise themselves by hunting them, and are hardened by this toil. Those who kill most receive great praise when they exhibit the horns as trophies of their success. These uri, however, even when young, cannot be tamed. In the expanse of their horns, as well as in form and appearance, they differ much from our domesticated oxen." Although this is something of an exaggeration as to the size of the aurochs, it was a tremendous animal, standing fully six feet high at the shoulder, as is proved by complete skeletons found in bogs. The aurochs was well known in Germany in the Middle Ages, and frequent references are found to it under the name of "ur." It is often compared or contrasted with the "wisent," which was (and still is) the European bison. The ur is mentioned in the famous Nibelungenlied, in which the hero Siegfried is said to have killed four, with a wisent and an elk. Aurochs horns were mounted in silver and used as drinking horns by the ancient Germans. After these animals became rare, these mighty horns, which were often more than six feet long, were prized as curiosities and as historic relics. The most famous of these horns were preserved in castles and inns in south Germany, some until a comparatively recent date.

After its disappearance from Germany, probably by the year 1400, the aurochs still lived in the forests of Poland and Lithuania. In the fifteenth and sixteenth centuries the hunting of the ur was a special privilege of the princes of Masovia, a district not far from Warsaw, and from their family records we learn of the decline of the ur. One of the curious old figures of the aurochs is in a book of travels by Sigismund von Herberstein, published about the year 1550. This gentleman had traveled widely in Poland as an envoy of the emperor; he was greatly surprised and impressed by the existence of the huge aurochs and wisent in the royal game preserves of the Polish princes, and brought with him to Vienna a skin of each. These he

26

MOST CATTLE ARE BELIEVED TO HAVE

DESCENDED FROM THE MASSIVE AUROCHS

THE HEREFORD IS TYPICAL OF THE MODERN BEEF BREEDS

had stuffed, and set up in the hall of his house in Vienna, in what was apparently one of the first real attempts at the art of taxidermy, now so highly developed by modern museums. By the year 1564, the last herd of the aurochs near Warsaw seems to have been reduced to about forty head; in 1599 there were only twenty-four, and in 1602 these were reduced to four. The last solitary cow died in 1627, ending the record of this great ancestor of our domestic breeds.

From the finest and most trustworthy figure of the aurochs preserved to us, which is copied on the margin of this page, and from various historic sources, we know that the adult bull aurochs was nearly black, with a light stripe down the middle of the back, and probably lighter underneath and on the inner sides of the legs. The calves, and probably the cows, were red, and there has been some speculation as to the existence in ancient times of a red race of the aurochs in the Black Forest of Germany. The change of color from red in the calves to black in the adult is found in various degrees in other types of wild cattle. The powerful form of the aurochs is preserved in the bulls of many modern breeds, like the Holstein or Brown Swiss. It did not have a high shoulder hump like the bison, nor the bison's shaggy mane. The enormous horns extended straight sidewise from the skull, then curved forward and a little upward. They were light colored but with black tips.

The aurochs was well known in western Asia in ancient times, and this is thought to be the region where it was first domesticated. A pair of wonderful golden cups found at Amyclae, near Sparta, in Greece, gives us the best evidence of this domestication. These were found in ruins clearly of the Mycenian period, which comes before written Grecian history, and the date may be set at about 1500 B.C. The figures on one of these cups show

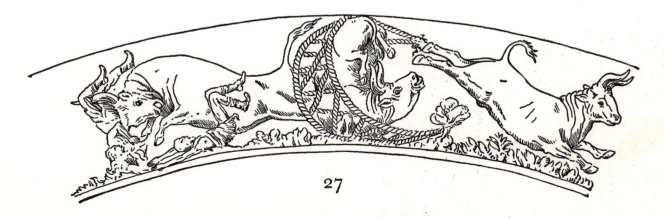

27

the capture of the wild aurochs with nets, and on the other the tamed bulls and cows, one of them bellowing as it is driven forward by a man who has a rope around its hind foot. These spirited figures are the finest of all representations of the aurochs that have been preserved to us. In Assyrian and Babylonian times the aurochs was hunted from chariots, and various relief figures agree exactly with what we know of this animal from other sources. It was shown in the Assyrian figures from the side, consequently with the horns in line. In copying these figures at Persepolis, the Persians, who did not know the animal itself, modified these figures, which were only apparently one-horned, into a "unicorn"; and "unicorn" appears again in the Latin translation of the Old Testament, for the Hebrew "reem." This was an unfortunate mistake, copied in both the English King James version and in Martin Luther's German translation. It is quite clear that the Hebrew word refers to the wild aurochs, hunted by the neighbors of the Jewish peoples, and present in the Lebanon mountains, where its bones have been found in caves.

The domestication of the aurochs dates far back into prehistoric times and appears to have taken place somewhere in western Asia. The men of the New Stone Age seem to have entered Europe from the east, and to have brought their distinctive domestic animals with them. These included a domestic ox, whose bones are easily distinguished from that of the giant aurochs of the forest by their smaller size and by the different shape of the skull, with short sidewise pointing horns. This earliest domestic race of cattle is usually known as the Celtic shorthorn; but it must be remembered that it is not especially closely related to the well-known modern "shorthorn," which is a breed developed in quite modern times. Except for the skull and its smaller size, the bones of the Celtic shorthorn agree in every

28

detail with those of the aurochs. There does not seem to have been any new attempt to domesticate the aurochs in Europe, but there may have been occasional crossing between the domestic cattle and the wild cattle of the forest. The remains of the domestic cattle increase in the refuse heaps of early man (the "kitchen middens"), while the bones of the aurochs decrease. The bones of the Celtic shorthorn are found from Scotland to the south of Europe; and this variety is quite evidently the ancestor of most of our modern breeds of cattle.

In several domestic animals there is much evidence that our modern breeds may bear the blood of more than one wild ancestor. The aurochs was the principal ancestor of the domestic cattle of western Asia, which spread to Europe with the invasions of some of the peoples of the New Stone Age. Many of the African domestic cattle, and among them those of the ancient Egyptians, seem to be plainly derived from the very different Indian zebu. Some of the earliest known figures show that they were humped like the zebu, and, except for the hornless breed, developed in Egypt as early as 3000 B.C., they have the upward directed horns of the Indian cattle. The zebu is a wholly domestic creature, and none of the existing wild cattle of southeastern Asia can be thought to be its direct ancestor. Its nearest wild ancestor must be sought among forms extinct before historic times, as is the case for the camel also. One of its most striking characteristics, the extension of the dewlap (the fold of skin along the lower side of the neck) to the chin, is not matched in any wild type of the ox tribe, though it is developed in the half domestic Indian gayal. The long dewlap and the hump can be seen in some of the earliest Assyrian representations of domestic cattle. It is noteworthy that the voice of the zebu is different from that of our familiar breeds.

These cattle with upright horns spread southward through Abyssinia in early times, and later throughout northeastern Africa, and through the Sudan region south of the Sahara to west Africa. The numerous cattle of Madagascar are also derived from this east African stock. Some of the modern African breeds are spectacular for their enormous horns, and are favorites in zoological gardens. This long-horned stock was brought to Spain at an early date, probably by the Phoenicians. It apparently has completely mingled there with aurochs races to form the Spanish breeds. It probably reached Italy at a later date, and in modern times is most clearly preserved in the modern Italian breed and in the steppe cattle of Hungary. The shaggy highland cattle of Scotland may have some relation to this type, judging from the shape of their horns.

It is only fair to add that some zoologists believe that the breeds with long and upright horns, including the zebu itself, are also derived from the Asiatic aurochs. They regard the long dewlap of the zebu, and its other characteristics, as developed by domestication. It is true that the "hump" on the zebu's back is only a mass of fat not supported by the backbone, and that it is present in some of the African zebu-like breeds and absent in others. This is a question which needs to be studied still more. The Indian zebu resists a good many tropical diseases, and it has been brought to Brazil and to our southern states, and especially to Texas. A big zebu bull certainly looks astonishingly different from any of our usual types of cattle.

In England and Scotland there are a few very distinct herds famous as "wild cattle." The best known of these wild herds is that of Chillingham Park, which seems to have maintained itself for hundreds of years, probably at least since the enclosure of the forest in the thirteenth century. These cattle are white with black or red ears and muzzles, and with some black in

30

Percy Reeves

MANY TYPES OF DOMESTIC CATTLE IN AFRICA AND ASIA HAVE HUMPS

THE JERSEY COW GIVES THE RICHEST MILK

the legs. Some of the older writers about domestic animals thought that these "wild" cattle of the English parks were direct descendants of the aurochs. It is now quite certain that they are really the *feral* race produced by escaped cattle of the prehistoric Celtic shorthorn breed. There is some mention of such feral herds of domestic cattle in the forest laws of King Canute (1014-1035 A.D.). Most modern breeds are of a later date.

Only a small number of the breeds of cattle have been brought to America. We are likely to think of them as divided into two main types. There are the more slenderly built dairy breeds, like the Jersey and Guernsey, the Ayrshire, and the Holstein, and the heavier, deeper bodied beef breeds, represented by the modern shorthorn, the Hereford, and the Aberdeen Angus. In Europe there are a great many other breeds, many of them quite local, often used for both milk and beef, and entirely unknown to us in America. We are acquainted with the Spanish long-horned cattle, for these were brought to America by Columbus, and when introduced into Mexico, developed the great herds of longhorns which were familiar in the southwestern United States in the cowboy era. The tremendous horns of these wild cattle, which may have a spread of seven feet, are different from both the zebu and from the aurochs type, and seem to come from the combination of the two in the Spanish cattle. These longhorns are now almost extinct, but we hope that the State of Texas may give them a reservation, and preserve the breed for the sake of its historic interest. Hornless (or "polled") races of cattle arise by the chance appearance of hornless individuals. If these are bred together, the tendency to produce horns can easily be eliminated. An ancient hornless Egyptian breed has already been mentioned. In the modern breeds, the Aberdeen Angus is hornless, and there is a polled sub-breed of the Hereford.

31

If we look at any travel book about the Philippines, Siam, or any of the Malay countries, we are sure to see pictures of the water buffalo. This is no relative of our American buffalo, which is misnamed and is truly a *bison*, and has a European relative now almost extinct, so that they are properly called the American and the European bisons. The water buffalo is directly derived from a wild species still found in the forests of India and Ceylon. These true buffalos have horns which are triangular in cross-section, and black in color. Some specimens of the wild race have enormous horns. The domesticated race spread westward through Persia and Mesopotamia to Egypt in early historic times. It was introduced in Italy about the year 600, and is the common ox of the south of the peninsula. It is in use also in the countries of the Balkan Peninsula.

CHAPTER FIVE
Sheep and their Wild Cousins

ONE of the most difficult problems in the history of domestic animals is the question of the ancestry of the sheep. There is a bewildering variety of breeds, and the changes produced by domestication have been especially marked. While cats and dogs, horses, donkeys, cattle, goats, and swine, are all able to return to a wild life, which we refer to as becoming *feral*, and have done so in various parts of the world, sheep are almost entirely incapable of such a feral life, and have become completely dependent on man. This is a logical final result of domestication. We may be sure that our domestic sheep came from the wild sheep of Europe and Asia, for the only other places where any wild sheep exist are the Rocky Mountains in North America, and the North African mountains, and we are certain that neither our American bighorn nor the African Barbary sheep enter into the origin of the domestic breeds. There are several distinct types of wild sheep in Asia and a single species in Europe (the moufflon), and it will be interesting to compare the principal types of domestic sheep with these wild relatives.

One of the main difficulties in the way of tracing the ancestry of our domestic sheep lies in the fact that most of them are long-tailed, while all of the wild species are short-tailed. It is quite clear, however, from a survey of the different modifications of the tail, that lengthening of the tail is a

characteristic which has appeared with domestication, like lop ears, and that in some cases (as in the fat-tailed sheep) it may have been selected as a desirable character in the same way that the hairy wild type has been converted into the woolly domestic form.

Darwin's great book on the "Variation of Animals and Plants under Domestication," published seventy years ago, left the problem of the origin of the sheep unsolved. In his day the scientists who had studied the sheep thought that there were from six to fourteen wild types mixed up in our modern domestic races. A great deal of attention has been paid to this problem since Darwin's time, but we are still forced to conclude that three or more wild species have been drawn upon for domestication; and as these have been crossed and intermixed, we may have a single modern breed descended from several wild forms. This is the opposite of the normal course of evolution, or indeed of the production of domestic races, and it could only take place under the artificial and partly abnormal conditions of domestication. The same fusion of several wild species into the domesticated form is seen in other domestic animals, especially in the dog and in the long-horned cattle.

Sheep have a well-defined character which is as much proverbial as that of the donkey or the mule. In sheep, timidity and docility, combined with a gentle stupidity, are carried to such an extreme that the animals are pitifully helpless in emergencies, and are given to panics which involve the whole flock and may be disastrous. They seem to be the least intelligent and the least teachable of all the domestic four-footed animals. This combination of mental characteristics is plainly the result of selection by man, and is connected with the keeping of sheep in such immense flocks that independence of behavior is a disadvantage to the shepherd. Evolution of the

34

sheep in this direction does, however, seem to have gone too far, for it is the widespread practice to keep a few goats with a flock of sheep. The goats keep the sheep from stampeding, fight off dogs, and are almost ridiculously respected as leaders by the sheep.

The importance of sheep to primitive pastoral peoples was and is very great. They depend on their flocks for meat, wool, tallow, skins, and milk, and occasionally make a less familiar use of them as beasts of burden, or in agriculture to tread seed into the soil in freshly sown fields.

The use of sheep for milk production is unfamiliar to us, but is widespread among primitive peoples and is still found in a few isolated regions in civilized countries. Roquefort cheese is a product of ewe's milk which is still well known, and though the modern American imitation of this type of cheese is made from cows' milk, "sheep dairying" is still carried on in the French countryside surrounding the little town of Roquefort, from which the cheese takes its name. It is amusing to learn that the ultra-modern milking machine has been introduced in Roquefort for milking these ewes.

Turning to the history of domestication of the sheep, we learn that it was one of the earliest of domestic animals to appear in Egyptian history, and that it was independently domesticated by the men of the New Stone Age in Europe and elsewhere. The first Egyptian representation of the sheep appears on one of the earliest sculptures known, nearly 4000 B.C. It was a curious creature with long legs and sharply twisted but straight horns, which extended straight sidewise, and with a mane of long hair on the chest and neck. These sheep are often shown in sculptures of a later date being driven across newly sown fields to tread in the grain. Changes under domestication in this type of sheep may be followed for two thousand years in the Egyptian records, supported by evidence from sheep preserved as

35

mummies. These sheep, which probably had little or no wool mixed with their goat-like hair, began to diminish in numbers in the 12th dynasty, about 2000 B.C., when the fat-tailed, wool-bearing sheep was introduced from southwestern Asia. In the next 500 years, the older type disappeared from Egypt entirely.

A good many long-legged breeds still found in the Sudan and in North Africa seem to be closely allied to the ancient Egyptian breed. One of the most striking of these is kept by the Dinka tribes along the upper Nile, and hence is called the Dinka sheep. The wild relative of the straight-horned sheep must have been an Asiatic form; but while it may well have been derived, like several other types of sheep, from the urial of central Asia, the intermediate steps are unknown, and the ancestor of this sheep remains a problem. There are still breeds of sheep with horns much like those of the ancient Egyptian type, except that they do not extend straight sidewise, in Rumania and Hungary.

The first domestic sheep of Europe was brought by the same New Stone Age tribes who had domesticated the ox, and we feel quite sure that it was derived from the Asiatic moufflon, a wild sheep still found in Asia Minor and the Caucasus. This wild sheep is closely allied to the European moufflon, but is redder and has a somewhat different twist to its horns. There may already have been some of the blood of the Asiatic urial in this sheep before it was brought to Europe, for it was a fully domesticated form as shown by the fact that its tail had already been increased in length. This sheep is most familiar under the name of "Peat Sheep," since it is found in deposits of peat over much of northern Europe. Its remains are abundant in the deposits in the Swiss lakes left by the Lake Dwellers; these give us a good deal of information about its size and general appearance, but zoolo-

36

ROCKY MOUNTAIN SHEEP

MOUFFLON

SHEEP HAVE BECOME MOST TIMID AND DEFENSELESS

gists must feel sad that they can no longer study this type in living examples, for there were small flocks of a sheep directly descended from the peat sheep in parts of Switzerland until the middle of the last century. The loss of so ancient a form of domestic animals is scarcely less a zoological tragedy than the extinction of a wild species like the quagga or like the passenger pigeon at the hand of man.

A more primitive type of sheep, to judge from its short tail, appears at a later date in the Lake Dweller deposits, about at the beginning of the Bronze Age. This can best be accounted for as a new domestication from the European moufflon. The moufflon, now confined to Sardinia and Corsica, was formerly more widespread in Europe, and while it can be tamed only imperfectly, it breeds freely in captivity. Fortunately we are not limited to the bones of this domestic race for our knowledge of it since there can be no doubt that the short-tailed and short-wooled sheep found in isolated parts of Europe, and especially on islands where its populations have been preserved from intermixture with the improved mainland types, is directly descended from it.

The most moufflon-like and least modified of these short-tailed sheep appears to be the sheep of the uninhabited Island of Soa, near St. Kilda, the outermost of the Outer Hebrides, northwest of Scotland. The horns of the ram are startlingly like those of the moufflon, and the ewes are hornless. The general coloration is like that of the moufflon; and the only essential difference between the wild animal and the feral Soa sheep lies in the short wool of the latter. The island is visited once or twice a year by residents of St. Kilda who hunt down the Soa sheep with dogs and shear them. Otherwise these sheep are wild, and thus form an exception to the general failure of sheep to form feral races. This still further shows that they are nearer their wild ancestry than most sheep. The Soa sheep is a real relic of the past. Its preservation on a remote island is exactly like the preservation of many kinds of wild animals on islands, where they are spared from the competition of more modern forms, or from destruction by man.

Short-tailed sheep variously modified from the Soa type are found on the Isle of Man, in the Orkneys, Faroes, Iceland, and in a few places on the Continent of Europe. In Germany the barren heath-covered plains harbor a hardy short-legged and short-tailed "heath sheep." In some places, as in Iceland and the Hebrides, the rams of these sheep are especially likely to have multiple horns, four-horned rams are common, and even six-horned ones have been known. Multiple-horned sheep are also known in other parts of the world.

There is not much doubt that the wool-bearing sheep with down-curved horns, which displaced the ancient long-legged and straight-horned Egyptian sheep, beginning about the year 2000 B.C., came from southwestern Asia and were derived from the urial, or steppe sheep. The word "steppe" means grassy open plains. The urial is an inhabitant of the whole central Asian steppe region. It lives in large flocks, and is much less a mountain animal than the moufflon or the big-horned sheep. Most of our familiar breeds are plainly derived from this wild form, which has given rise also to the very distinct fat-tailed sheep, and probably to the fat-rumped sheep as well.

One of the main types of the domesticated urial which is of especial historical importance is the merino. This is a breed with a surpassing quality and amount of wool, from which many modern sub-breeds are derived. The merino seems to have originated in Asia Minor about the eighth century B.C., and to have been spread by the Phoenicians into North Africa and

Spain. It is likely that it spread more slowly across southern Europe to reach Spain a second time from the north. The merino is characterized by a reddish and oily skin, and long, fine, and very dense wool. The skin is often very much folded, which increases the wool-bearing surface. The ewes are usually hornless, while the rams have good-sized spiral horns. The breed is little valued for mutton, and is not much improved by good pasture or grain feeding. It is best suited to such modern sheep-raising territories as South Africa, southern South America, and Australia.

A second great group of breeds derived from the urial is that of the fat-tailed sheep. These are found in western Asia and Africa, and appear to have arisen by selection for the increased masses of fat in the tail, which were of special importance to peoples who did not use the pig. This seems to have been the common breed kept by the ancient Hebrews in Palestine in their nomadic stage. It attracted the attention of the Greek traveler Herodotus, and of the scientist Aristotle. There is an ancient travelers' tale that some of these sheep were so helpless that their heavy tails had to be bound on a little cart which they pulled behind them. The weight of the tail may amount to 40 lbs., or more than a fourth of the total weight of the animal. Some of these sheep may be quite short-tailed, while others have tails which sweep the ground, and still others have the tail bent sharply upward. They all have the underside of the tail bare. The Caracul sheep is the fat-tailed breed most familiar to us, on account of the very beautiful curly hair of the new-born lambs, whose skins continue to be important in the fur trade to the present day.

The very long-tailed African and Arabian breeds which do not have an accumulation of fat in the tail are probably also directly related to the urial.

The last of the main types of domestic sheep is the fat-rumped sheep of

central Asia. This is the type kept by all of the nomadic peoples from the Khirghiz steppes of south Russia to eastern Siberia, Mongolia, and China. It is their principal domestic animal, and is kept in vast flocks, sometimes numbering 20,000. The unit of value in central Asia is a one-year-old lamb. These sheep have been thought to be derived from the big-horned sheep of the mountains of Asia, but it seems quite as likely that they are still another independent domestication of the urial.

The wild big-horned sheep of Asia are closely allied to our more familiar Rocky Mountain sheep. The largest of them is the Marco Polo sheep of the high Pamir plateau, which has magnificent spiral horns. These forms do not seem to have been domesticated, but the large horns of some Tibetan breeds are thought to indicate some admixture of the big-horn blood.

CHAPTER SIX
Tame and Wild Goats

THE ancestry of the goats is as easy to determine as that of the sheep is difficult. The goat group is distinguished from the sheep group by the presence of a beard, by the absence of the foot glands which sheep have, by the strong smell of the bucks, and by differences in horns and skeleton. They ordinarily do not have an undercoat of wool like that of the sheep, and differ strikingly in mental characteristics, such as intelligence, independence, and ability to fend for themselves and take their own part in a fight.

There are two main types of goats, the more ordinary ones with simply curved horns and the Angora and Egyptian type with twisted horns, and these two types probably came from different ancestors. Goats are nearly as ancient in domestication as sheep, but they have not produced nearly so many breeds, nor, except for some of the milk-producing types, such extremely modified breeds. They do exhibit a remarkable tendency to the development of distinct races in different mountain ranges, exactly as the wild goats have developed distinct types in the principal mountains of Europe and Asia.

The hardiness of goats in comparison with sheep is remarkable. Out of 576 common European plants offered to them, goats ate 449 kinds, while sheep would eat only 327. No domestic animal becomes feral more quickly. Their pugnacious character is familiar and contrasts strongly with that of

the sheep. They will not allow a dog to drive them and are able to defend themselves successfully against all except the largest enemies.

As is the case with the sheep, domestication of the goat goes back to its introduction from Asia Minor into Europe by the men of the New Stone Age. The wild ancestor of these first goats was plainly the paseng, a type of wild goat still found on the Island of Crete, and in the mountains of Asia Minor and Persia. The arrival of the Stone Age goat in Europe seems to have been a little later than that of the sheep. In the deposits of the Lake Dwellers, in Switzerland (of a later age than the first introduction), goat remains are at first much more numerous. Later on, as these people developed their culture and presumably their security from attack, the remains of sheep began to take the place of those of the goat. The "peat goat," known from these remains, was a small creature which has apparently left no descendents in Europe, but the dwarf goat of Africa is believed to be descended from it. The record of the domestication of the goat in Egypt goes back to the earliest times.

The dwarf goat of Africa seems to be little changed in appearance in the six thousand years which have passed since it was first recorded. It stands only about eighteen inches high at the shoulder, and is less than thirty inches long. It has short horns, three or four inches long, in both sexes. In spite of their small size these goats are courageous in the extreme, and one comes to the aid of another if he sees the other in distress. It is amusing to learn that they are spread over most of Africa, and that in the flat terrain of that vast continent, these goats have transferred their mountain climbing instincts to climbing in trees. They may be seen in small troops, twenty or thirty feet from the ground, in the top of a low tree, some feeding on the leaves of the tree, others enjoying the shade, while some stretch out on a limb to sleep. Some dwarf goats are found also in Arabia, India, and Siberia.

At the end of the New Stone Age, at the same time with the new domestication of the moufflon, the dwarf goat was replaced in Europe by a larger animal, which evidently represents a new domestication from the same wild species of Asia Minor. This Bronze Age goat is evidently the ancestor of most of the modern European breeds. Its descendents are the common, rather nondescript goats that are found everywhere in dry, tropical countries, apparently introduced from Spain. These goats are kept for their flesh and skins. The more highly developed breeds of goats in central Europe, which have been selected since prehistoric times as milk producers, are very different creatures produced by careful selection.

Turning to the description of the wild goat of Persia and Asia Minor, which is so clearly directly allied to the common domestic goat, we find a somewhat larger animal, which may stand as much as three feet high at the shoulder. The wild goat is brownish gray in winter, changing to yellowish or reddish brown in summer. The horns of the buck are curved backward, with a knobbed but sharp front edge, and they may reach a length of more than three feet. The horns of the does are shorter, similar in shape to those of the male, but with a smooth front edge. The wild goat is an extremely active animal, living in the rocky and mountainous parts of the countries it inhabits. The bucks and does band together into small flocks, and graze above the limits of forest in the mountains. They post sentinels while grazing to watch for approaching enemies, and not only take turns in performing this duty, but seem to have a regular order of turns, beginning with the younger animals and ending with the senior buck.

This habit of standing watch makes hunting wild goats an especially

difficult sport. In Asia Minor the Turkish hunters, who have driven their domestic animals down from the mountains for the winter, and have taken care of the last of their field work for the season, turn their attention to hunting the wild goat. Shooting four or five goats during the winter is regarded as a successful season's hunt. The flesh is greatly prized, both roasted fresh and dried in long strips like what we call "jerked" meat in America. The long-hair pelts are used for prayer rugs, and are valued especially on account of their pungent goat smell. The horns are worked up into knife hilts and powder horns. The most curious object for which these animals are valued is the "bezoar stone," which is occasionally found in their stomachs. This is a ball of hair and other matter which forms in the stomachs of animals which chew the cud, like goats, sheep, and cattle, and which becomes hard and smooth from being polished in the stomach. Such hair balls may form in the stomachs of other kinds of animals, but they do not seem to become smooth. The bezoar stones were superstitiously valued in the Middle Ages for supposed medicinal properties, and especially as an antidote against poison. They still retain some of this valuation in the Orient, and it is believed that they are found in the stomachs of wild goats more frequently than in any other animal.

It has been already mentioned that goats become wild very easily; only the domestic cat can return to the independent life of a wild creature so promptly and successfully. It was the custom in the sixteenth and seventeenth centuries, and even in the eighteenth, to carry a few goats, sheep, pigs, and even cattle, on shipboard. Specimens of these animals were often released on uninhabited islands with the idea that they would serve as food for some shipwrecked crew in the future. Goats were thus released on many remote islands. One of the most famous of these colonies of goats is the one

Percy Reeves

THE WILD GOAT OF ASIA MINOR AND PERSIA
IS THE ANCESTOR OF THE DOMESTIC BREEDS

THE GOAT IS BOLD AND BRAVE LIKE HIS ANCESTORS

on the Island of Juan Fernandez in the southern Pacific, where the feral goats were the companions of Alexander Selkirk, whose adventures gave rise to the famous story of "Robinson Crusoe." Goats were released on that island in 1572 by its discoverer, the Spanish explorer Juan Fernandez, for whom the island is named.

Sometimes the release of goats brings an unforeseen calamity. The uninhabited Island of Guadelupe off the coast of California was covered with a thick mat of trees and bushes and had a considerable number of peculiar birds and animals which were found nowhere else in the world. The goats released on Guadelupe destroyed so much of the plant life that rains finished the work, and the whole island was presently washed bare, and its life exterminated before scientists had even had an opportunity to study it. The feral goats on the Island of St. Helena in the South Atlantic also contributed greatly to the destruction of its vegetation and animal life, which would have been of the greatest scientific interest.

Everyone in this country rides almost every day on cushions made from the hair of a kind of goat, namely the Angora goat, whose long lustrous hair is known as mohair, and is used for the manufacture of plush, which covers the seats in railway coaches and autos. These Angora goats and a few related breeds look quite different from the common goat, most of all in their strongly twisted horns, especially in the old males. It is not very likely that this remarkable distinct type of goat could be derived from the common domestic goat or from the Persian wild goat.

The great twisted-horned goat of the Himalaya Mountains, known as the markhoor, was thought for a long time to be the ancestor of the Angora type. It was observed, however, that the horns of the markhoor twist in the opposite direction from that of the Angora goat, and furthermore, that

45

in the hybrid offspring of the markhoor with domestic goats of any type, the horns always have the markhoor twist. This must mean that our Angora goat could not be directly descended from the markhoor. There is no living wild species of goat which is directly related to the Angora type. Remains of a fossil type of goat have been found in Europe, however, in which the twist of the horns corresponds to that of the Angoras. The place of domestication of this type of goat could scarcely have been in Europe, since these goats have not spread north of the Alps even to the present day. It is fairly certain that this is another of the familiar domestic animals that came from western Asia, and probably from Asia Minor. The Angora goat has a well-known relative in the Kashmir goat, whose woolly coat is made into the finest and most valuable cloth known. A genuine Kashmir shawl may cost more than 700 dollars.

There is an extremely ancient picture of a twisted horned goat on an ancient Babylonian seal, which shows the erect ears and the straight profile of what may be supposed to be the primitive type of this goat. Goats of this kind appeared much later in Egypt than the common goat, and by the time of the 12th Dynasty (about 2000 years B.C.), these goats had developed the strongly convex nose and face of the modern Egyptian goat, together with the long hanging ears which seem always to be a mark of domestication. The most extreme type of this hump-nosed goat is called the mamber goat, and has spread into southeastern Europe. In the other direction, goats with twisted horns have spread to China, where very large numbers of their skins come on the market.

There are various other types of wild goats which may be regarded as close relatives of the domestic goats. One of these types is the "Thur," of which one species is found in the Pyrenees in Spain, and one in the Mountains of

46

the Caucasus. The ibexes form another group, with a distinct species in each of the great mountain ranges from the Pyrenees to the Himalaya, with an extra species in Abyssinia. The ibexes have magnificent knobby horns which reach a length of five feet in the species of the Thian Shan Mountains of Central Asia. The Barbary sheep, which inhabits the Atlas Mountains of Morocco and Algeria, is remarkable for the great mane of long hair on its throat, breast, and front legs. It combines characteristics of both the sheep and the goats, and must be regarded as a distinct type. The bharal or blue sheep of Tibet, is another mountain animal about equally related to the sheep and goats.

CHAPTER SEVEN
The Ancestry of the Horse

THE disappearance of horses from the streets of cities, and from the roads and even from the fields in the country, has been one of the most important changes in our daily life in very recent times, with the coming of the auto, truck and tractor. To the farmer horses had been for ages next only to cattle in importance. Their former place even in city life is shown by the great number of swift breeds developed for pulling carriages and of heavy breeds for trucking. New gasoline and Diesel engines have reduced the horses in the United States to about half of their former numbers.

We are so familiar with the appearance of the horse that we are likely to forget that it is one of the most remarkable of living creatures. Horses actually walk and run on the tips of their fingers and toes. We can understand easily enough that this should be the case in an animal made for swiftness, since we run on our toes ourselves; and though they might not especially like the comparison, our ballet dancers are even able to dance on the tips of their toes. The common names of the joints in the horse's legs are misleading. The horseman calls what is really the wrist, in the front leg, the "knee"; the true knee, in the hind leg, is called the "stifle"; the heel is called the "hock," and what is called the heel is the back of the hoof, and does not in the least correspond to the heel of any other animal. If we begin at the shoulder and hip, we can easily see that the joints in a horse's legs are arranged in exactly

the same order as in our own arms and legs, and that the difference is almost entirely in the length of the bones of the hand and foot.

By studying the fossil remains of animals of past ages, scientists have learned more and more about the history of the horse tribe. The terraces of the dry plains bordering the Rocky Mountains have produced the greatest number of bones of these extinct horses. I wonder if you realize that the search for fossils is one of the most exciting things in the world. So many fossil horses have been found that their history has become a classic example of evolution for textbooks of biology. If you will open such a book, or best of all, if you can visit one of the great museums of natural history in this country, you may read this story or find some of the actual evidence on which it is based.

We learn that the horses, donkeys, and zebras are really very closely alike, and form the horse group. The only living relatives of this group are the tapirs and rhinoceroses, which at first glance do not look in the least like horses. When we study their skeletons, we find that the tapirs and rhinoceroses have the middle toe of each foot strengthened and supported on a hoof, and that the single toe of the horse corresponds with this middle hoof. Fossil rhinoceroses and tapirs are still more like the ancient horses, which also had more than one toe. This toe arrangement is quite different from the foot of the ox, the sheep, the deer, or the pig, which have a pair of hoofs. Scientists call the horses and their allies the "odd-toed" hoofed animals, while the ox and related animals are "even-toed."

The record of the fossils connects our modern one-toed horses step by step with the three-toed and then with four-toed ancestors. In this group the "missing links" have been found. The four-toed horse, called "eohippus" by the scientists (meaning "dawn horse"), was a small creature no

bigger than a fox. The change from four short toes to one long one goes with a steady increase in size and with a wonderful improvement in the molar grinding apparatus. The whole change consists in improvements for swift running on open plains. As the horse's running powers increased, more and more energy (in the form of food) had to be supplied; and the more powerful jaws and complicated teeth were absolutely necessary to go with the longer legs. The development of the horse for swift running accompanied the change from the low forests of North America in the time of eohippus to the high open plains of our modern West. Fossil horses are found in Europe and Asia as well as in the western United States, while the living wild members of the horse tribe are found only in Asia and Africa. One of the most surprising facts learned from the history of the horse is that while its principal development took place in America, every horse disappeared from the plains before the arrival of the American Indians; and this disappearance was so complete and sudden that we believe it must have been due to some contagious disease or some fatal parasite spread by insects.

If we turn from the history of the horse tribe in general to the history of our domestic horse, we find that our European ancestors of the Old and New Stone Ages were well acquainted with wild horses. So many horses were used for food by the men of the earliest part of the New Stone Age, that vast bone heaps, consisting almost entirely of horse remains with the long bones cracked for the marrow, have been found. One bone heap of this sort at Solutre, in the Rhone valley in southern France, is estimated to contain the remains of 100,000 horses. Domestication of these horses took place some time toward the end of the New Stone Age; but here the record is already obscure, for the Lake Dwellers of Switzerland may themselves have come from the east and may have brought a domestic horse with them.

The European wild horse continued to live in the forests of Germany and Scandinavia until historic times. One of the pagan practices of the ancient German tribes was the sacrifice of horses and the eating of their meat at religious ceremonial feasts, held in oak groves. To this day one may find a relic of horse worship in the horse skulls set on the gables of houses and barns in South Germany. St. Boniface, who brought Christianity to the Germans, seems to have permitted the eating of horseflesh by his converts; but this practice was finally forbidden by a special letter from the Pope in the year 732. Wild horses are believed to have persisted until the year 1600 in the Vosges Mountains on the western border of Alsace.

Tracing the wild horse eastward, we find that a small dun-colored wild pony, called the tarpan, was formerly abundant everywhere in South Russia and in Central Asia. The tarpans were hated by the farmers and landowners because they devoured their stacked hay and especially because the tarpan stallions constantly recruited domestic mares for their wild droves. For these reasons they were mercilessly pursued by the Russians and were completely exterminated by the year 1870. While there were droves of half domestic tarpans, it now seems certain that the original tarpan was a genuine wild species of horses, exterminated before it was realized that it was of scientific interest and importance.

Farther to the east, however, we find a true wild horse still living. It was discovered by the Russian explorer Przewalsky in 1879 in the northwestern corner of Mongolia. It is usually called "Przewalsky's horse," but if you cannot pronounce this name, it is quite correct to say "Asiatic wild horse." It is a small, stockily built and distinctly yellowish horse, with an erect mane and no forelock. There is usually a dark shoulder stripe and a dark stripe down the middle of the back. The species seems to be declining in

numbers, with only three droves left, which live in separate districts. Fortunately, living specimens have now been brought to Europe, and they thrive and breed both in captivity and under half-wild conditions on large estates. Experiments in crossing them with domestic breeds of horses prove clearly that they are true horses, for the hybrids are perfectly fertile, while hybrids with domestic donkeys and with the Asiatic wild ass are "mules," which do not breed. It is possible that Przewalsky's horse may be preserved in captivity long after the wild stock has disappeared.

Our domestic horse is different from this Asiatic wild horse in having a hanging mane and forelock, more hair on the tail, and much less tendency to shoulder and back stripes; it is probably directly derived from the European wild horse of the Bronze Age and the early historic period, which is now extinct as a wild form. Nevertheless, Przewalsky's horse is clearly the nearest living relative of the North European and Asiatic ponies and of most of the heavy European breeds as well. They are alike in having a rounded profile of the face, no pit in the skull below the eye, and a low set tail. The larger modern breeds are derived from a large type of horse developed in the Middle Ages to carry armored riders, as well as armor of their own, in war.

The famous Arab horses, and the closely related barbs of North Africa, are known from historic evidence to have given rise to most of the swift and slenderly built breeds of modern times. The Arabian horse differs from the horses we have described in having a straight or incurved profile, shallow pits on the skull below the eyes, and a high set tail. There are other significant characteristics in the skeleton, and it seems certain that these beautiful creatures are derived from a wild horse of the Asiatic deserts (now extinct) which was entirely distinct from the heavy set European wild horse.

PRZEWALSKY'S HORSE IS THE
ONLY TRUE WILD HORSE TODAY

LITTLE EOHIPPUS ANCESTOR OF HORSES
WAS ABOUT 12 INCHES HIGH
HAD 4 TOES FORWARD AND 3 IN REAR

SPLENDID SPECIMENS ARE ATTAINED THRU SELECTIVE BREEDING

The horse from which the Arab type is derived seems to have been domesticated in Central Asia or Persia more than 3000 years B.C., for it spread westward through southern Europe in the time of the Lake Dwellers. The first record of horses in Babylonia is at least as early as 2000 B.C., but as Babylonian history goes much further back, they must have been acquired from neighboring Persia. It is curious to learn that horses were wholly unknown in Egypt, where the ass had been domesticated from the earliest times, until the dynasty of the Shepherd Kings, who entered Egypt from Asia in 1680 B.C. After this time the horse was much favored in Egypt, and was used with the chariot in war, just as it was by the Assyrians and Babylonians. Spirited reliefs show the use of the chariot in lion and aurochs hunting by the Assyrians. The horse was little used by the pastoral Jews in the early stages of their history, but was familiar to them from their neighbors and from the attacks of their enemies. Solomon seems to have introduced the building of chariot roads in Palestine (about 1000 B.C.), and to have imported a great number of horses for his army from Egypt, paying 600 shekels of silver for a chariot and its horses and 150 shekels for a cavalry horse (a shekel being about half an ounce). Throughout ancient times horses seem to have been valued mainly for their usefulness in war.

Horses and chariots were in use in Greece at least a thousand years B.C., to judge from the account of their use in the siege of Troy. The skillful bareback riding shown in the frieze of the Parthenon must have been a later development. This use of the two-wheeled chariot must have spread over all of Europe, as we hear of it in Scandinavian mythology and in the struggles of the early Britons with the Romans.

The Arabs, strangely enough, did not use horses to any extent until about the time of Mohammed (570 to 632 A.D.). They were dependent on camels

before that time. Since then the horse has been more highly valued in Arabia than perhaps anywhere else in the world, and the Arabs have to their credit the development of the finest breed of swift horses in the world.

When our pioneer settlers in North America reached the western plains they found Indian tribes who were superb horsemen, riding bareback, and shooting with bow and arrow from horseback, exactly like the wild Tartar horsemen in Central Asia. More than that, the customs of the tribes centered in the use of the horse in hunting and war, and seemed to represent an age-old association of native man and wild horse. Actually, however, the true wild horses native to North America had completely disappeared from the plains before the arrival of the first Indians from Asia. The few horses that escaped from the Spanish explorers in Mexico before the year 1600 increased to vast droves of these feral horses which spread from Mexico to Canada, and became known as "mustangs." The Indians promptly learned to tame the mustang, and it was abundant in the West in our "cowboy era." The cross of the mustang with domestic horses is called the "bronco." Perhaps there are a few small droves of mustangs left in the Great Basin even at the present time.

In South America the horse had much the same history as in North America. When the first settlement at Buenos Aires failed in 1537, five stallions and seven mares were left behind; and even by the year 1600 these had increased to thousands on the grassy Pampas. Here also, they were domesticated by the Indians, who became expert horsemen like their North American cousins. Though the wild horses have long been exterminated, the cowboys of the South American plains, known as "Gauchos," are still famous for their horsemanship.

CHAPTER EIGHT

The Donkey and Other Relatives of the Horse

IF you had ever driven a donkey to market with a load on his back or if you had tried to catch one in a pasture, you would know why his name has become a byword and himself a standard of comparison for stupidity and stubbornness. Spirit and intelligence seem to have been sacrificed in his domestication, leaving his valuable qualities sure-footedness, the ability to survive on coarse fodder on which a horse would starve, and a sort of humble patience and loyalty. It is hard to tell whether donkeys are tough and obstinate because they have been starved and beaten, or whether they are abused on account of their disagreeable characteristics.

As a matter of fact, the customary and widespread low opinion of the donkey, evident in the English and German languages, does him some injustice. It seems to be based on his behavior in damp northern climates, which are unsuited to him; for the donkey is a true desert animal and as we reach the Mediterranean lands we find these animals not only in very much greater numbers, but learn that they are valued and bred for spirit and speed instead of for stupid resistance to abuse. In our own country there are many more donkeys in the South; and when we go to the West Indies or to Mexico, we find them as abundant as in Egypt.

The history of the domestic donkey is as plain and simple as that of the horse is obscure and complicated. Donkeys are directly related to the wild donkey (the Nubian wild ass) of North Africa. They were first domesticated in Egypt, where they were employed from the earliest times. Good figures of them are shown on slates of the First Dynasty, about 3400 B.C. Throughout their long history in North Africa the domestic breed seems to have had frequent infusions of the blood of this wild ancestor, and there is much less tendency toward the formation of distinct and numerous breeds of donkeys than, for example, of horses.

The Nubian wild donkey is a spirited and agile desert animal with the general gray color, light underparts, and the shoulder stripe familiar to our common beast of burden. The unstriped legs are also similar, though the frequent tendency to stripes on the legs has led some zoologists to think that the donkey is related to the Somali wild ass, which constantly has stripes. The Nubian and the Somali wild asses, found only in northeast Africa, are the only wild relatives of the donkey which resemble it in having long ears and being gray in color. The Nubian species is now almost extinct. In other parts of Africa the asses are replaced by zebras, and in Asia by the onager and its relatives. The Somali wild ass in its native deserts makes an impression of extraordinary lightness and grace of movement. Its hoofs are remarkable for their hardness and strength—qualities which are needed on the hard and stony ground. It is said to keep as fat on dry and sparse vegetation as a stall-fed horse.

From Egypt the use of the domestic donkey spread into southwestern Asia some time before the year 1000 B.C. The first mention of the ass in the Bible tells of Abraham riding on one from Beersheba to Mount Mordah. From patriarchal times on, it is evident that the ass was one of the most

Percy Reeves

THE WILD ASS OF NORTH AFRICA IS THE FORBEAR OF THE DONKEY

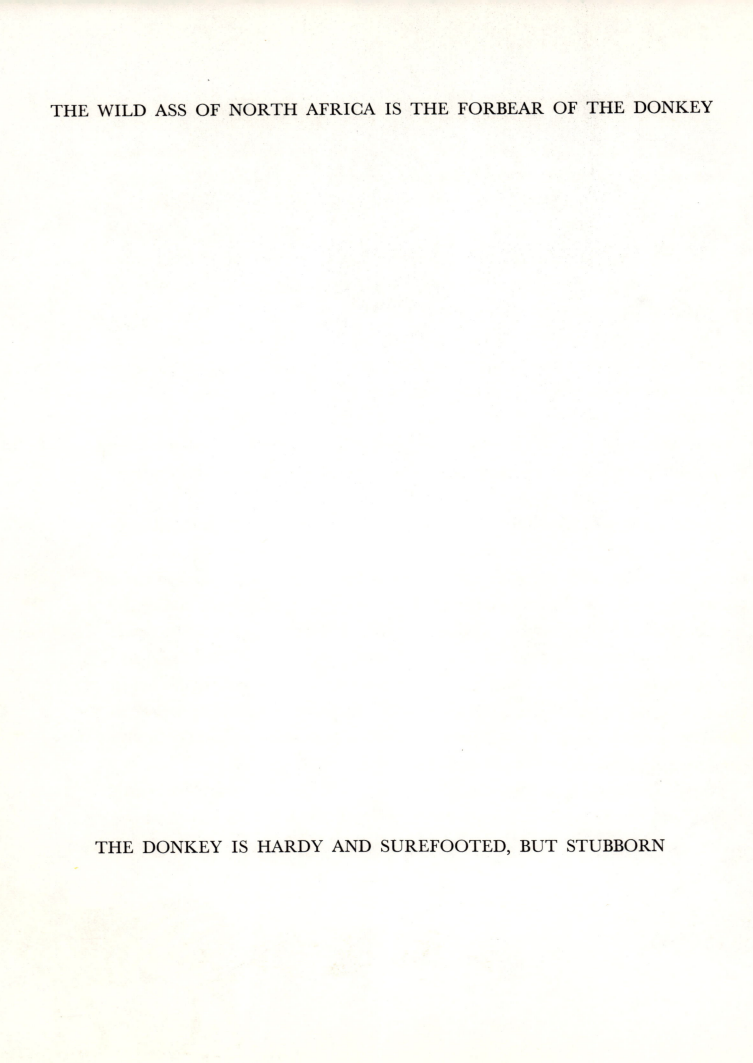

THE DONKEY IS HARDY AND SUREFOOTED, BUT STUBBORN

abundant domestic animals in Palestine. The fact that Jesus rode into Jerusalem on an ass is in accordance with the use of these creatures as saddle animals throughout the Near East. As saddle animals they have been bred for larger size, and the finest are nearly as large as horses and white or very pale in color. The domestic ass has spread throughout Central Asia and China, and via Persia and India to southeastern Asia and the East Indies. Wherever it is ridden bareback it is customary for the rider to sit far back on the haunches of his mount.

The handsome Asiatic wild asses, the onager in Syria and Arabia, the kulan of Mongolia, and the kiang of Tibet are all yellow instead of gray—tending to chestnut brown on the back in the kiang, and to paler tones in the onager. These three forms are different from the two African species in having short ears, and in general a more horse-like form. It is even yet quite uncertain whether or not they have ever been tamed, or whether their blood is infused into the domestic donkey.

The last group of the wild relatives of the horse—the zebra—is familiar to every visitor to the zoo or museum. No animal is more boldly striped than these creatures, and great scientific arguments have raged about their coloration—some believing that even such vivid stripes help to make the herds invisible at a distance; while others think that the zebra's pattern is interesting because suggestions of it are present in the Somali wild ass, and are occasional in donkeys and even in horses. We believe we can detect in this one of the general characteristics which show the relationship between the zebras, African wild asses, Asiatic wild asses, and horses, which compose the four principal divisions of the horse tribe.

There are several quite distinct kinds of zebras. One, the quagga of South Africa, was remarkable in being striped only on the head and front of the

body. It formerly existed in immense numbers in the whole territory south of the Orange River. It was hunted by the Boers for its flesh and its skins— the flesh being used as food for their black servants, and the skins to make sacks for grain. Before their relentless rifles the great droves of quagga melted away. Specimens were brought to the older European zoos and museums, but before there was any organized interest in the preservation of wild species; and, indeed, before it was realized what was happening, the quagga was extinct. The last wild quagga was shot more than seventy years ago.

Numerous other zebras with complete striping seem to be allied to the extinct quagga, and are best known by the Boer name "Bontequagga." Bontequaggas are found throughout the plains country of Africa north of the Transvaal and south of the Sahara. A broad-striped, heavy-headed, and long-eared zebra inhabits the mountains of Cape Colony. This is sometimes called the true zebra, because it was the first one to be given a scientific name, *"Equus zebra,"* by the Swedish naturalist, Linnaeus, who invented our system of naming animals.

The largest and most beautiful of all the zebras, of which a specimen was sent by the Emperor Menelik of Abyssinia to President Grevy of France in 1882, is known as Grevy's zebra. It is completely covered by narrow stripes. Although this noble animal was the last of the zebras to receive a scientific description, it was probably the first to become known in Europe. Zebras were known to the ancient Greeks and Romans as "hippotigres," meaning horse-tigers, and at least one specimen was exhibited in the Roman circus amphitheatre by the Emperor Caracalla, in the third century A.D. Other specimens reached Constantinople as gifts from Abyssinia, and one is said to have been sent to far-off Japan in the seventeenth century.

One of the most curious uses of the donkey is for the production of mules.

When a mare is bred to a jack (as the male donkey is called) the offspring which results is neither a horse nor an ass, but a mule. The mule has the size and power of the horse and the toughness and resistance to disease of the donkey; and, it must be admitted, receives from the male parent its obstinate disposition, which has become quite as proverbial as that of the donkey.

Mules have been known from very ancient times, as we learn of their use in the story of the siege of Troy; and they have been produced in all parts of the world where the horse and ass have been introduced. Mules were of very great commercial importance before the coming of machinery, and in remote and especially in mountainous regions, their sure-footedness, and strength make them indispensable for pack trains and for saddle animals.

The most remarkable thing about mules is that they are sterile, which means that they do not produce offspring at all. The horse and the ass have become so completely distinct that (except for the production of sterile mules) they cannot be mixed by interbreeding as, for example, the various breeds of horses can, or as the donkey and the wild ass can. In fact, if it were not for the one fact that the Przewalsky's horse will cross with the domestic horse, producing fertile offspring, and that it produces "mules" with the donkey, we might be uncertain as to whether it is more closely related to the true horse or to the Asiatic wild ass. Zebras have been crossed with both horses and donkeys, and produce "zebroids," which are likewise sterile. Mules have been so familiar for so long a time that the word "mule" is now often used for any hybrid between distinct species. The production of sterile hybrids (or the failure to breed together at all) is often taken as the simplest means of defining what we mean by a "species" of animal. The study of this whole subject of inheritance and hybridization is called *genetics*, and is one of the most important branches of the science of life.

59

CHAPTER NINE
Ancestry of Domestic Swine

THE wild swine of Europe still hold their own in a good many forested places on the Continent of Europe, and although they disappeared from the British Isles by about the year 1600, and have been much reduced in numbers in Germany and France in the last few hundred years, there is little danger that the famous "wild boar" will become extinct like the aurochs. No reasonable student of the breeds of the domestic pig doubts that so far as Europe is concerned, they are derived from the native wild species, which was everywhere at hand. In fact, the wild pig must have been tamed many times and in many different places in Europe and the near-by regions.

The wild boar is a strong and active creature, whose general form is so much like that of the domestic pig that we need not describe it. It reaches a shoulder height of three feet and a weight of more than four hundred pounds. Its body is covered with coarse hair, with an almost mane-like crest along the back. The head is larger and longer than that of the domestic pig, the feet are larger, the tusks longer and stronger, and the whole body is narrower. The general color is nearly black, with a mixture of gray and rusty brown on the body. The snout, ears, and lower parts of the legs are black. The ears, of course, are erect. The wild swine are extremely courageous and stubborn fighters, and are able to drive off most of their enemies, except man.

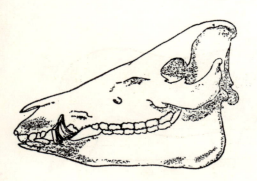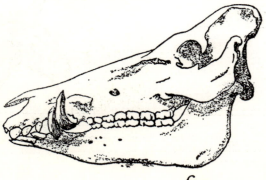

Percy Reeves

THE WILD BOAR FROM WHICH OUR PIG HAS DESCENDED STILL
ROAMS IN MANY PARTS OF EUROPE

THE PIG FURNISHES MANY USEFUL THINGS

Their bright color and striped pattern, with their alertness and liveliness, make a litter of young wild pigs one of the most pleasing sights. The mothers often join together in small droves, and the young piglets play and fight together. It is said that if one mother sow is killed, her companions will adopt her orphaned sucklings.

Hunting the wild boar has been regarded as a noble sport throughout history, even though it is known to the English in India as "pig-sticking." It is customary to hunt on horseback and with dogs, and to kill the quarry with a spear. In far-off Celebes, where I once hunted the wild boar and the babirusa myself, our Malay hunters were armed with short spears. Both sows and boars run from the hunting party until they find that they are unable to escape. Then they stand their ground and charge so suddenly and viciously that the hunter may be in danger from the sweeping tusks even on horseback.

Domestication of the pig, begun in the New Stone Age, had gone so far by the time of the Swiss Lake Dwellers that the peculiar shortening of the snout, with which we are familiar in some of our modern breeds, had already appeared. Swine seem to be especially variable under domestication, and especially amenable to human selection. The shortening of the snout may be carried to a ridiculous extreme, and hanging ears, which accompany domestication in so many other kinds of animals, are found in various stages of development. Unhappily, one of the first characteristics to be lost is the handsome striped pattern of the young. Traces of this may often be seen in mongrel litters of the domestic pig.

The domestic pig makes an early appearance in ancient Egyptian art, and appears in ancient times throughout western Asia. The prejudice against its use for sacrifice and for food among the ancient Jews seems to have spread to the Phoenicians, and is strengthened, if anything, among the modern Moslems. In spite of this prejudice, swine were kept even by the Jews, though perhaps never in very great numbers.

Pigs promptly go back to a wild life when they have the opportunity, and when they do become "feral," only a few generations are necessary before they have the long head and snout, the long legs, and the narrow body of the wild pig. Most pigs in the southern United States lead an almost entirely feral life. Wherever they occur it is necessary to fence them *out* of the fields and dooryards instead of fencing them into their own fields and pens, as we do in the North. These half wild pigs are known as "razorbacks," and their snouts are so long that there is an old joke about how to tell when one of them is fat enough to butcher. You hold him up by the ears, and if the body overbalances the snout, he is as fat as he will get.

I once lived in northwestern Louisiana, and on my tramps through the woods, often found good-sized square pens made with fence rails, which had a funnel-shaped opening. These were used to corral the pigs once a year to mark the ears of the young, so that some kind of ownership could be claimed. The feral pigs fiercely resent the presence of dogs, and of course it is almost impossible to drive them. A mongrel dog is consequently trained to run *from* the drove of pigs and lead them into the corral. He can then easily escape their clashing tusks by jumping over the rails; and the men, who have been hidden beside the wings of the V-shaped opening, fall in behind the pigs and close the gate.

In the East Indies and southeastern Asia we find a distinct kind of wild pig, easily distinguished by the absence of the crest of hair on the back, and a white streak along the sides of the face. There are a number of distinct kinds of these wild pigs on the different East Indian islands, and a bewildering

62

number of domestic races derived from them. In the case of the wild pig of New Guinea, which is quite different from the pigs of the nearest islands, it is suspected that it is really a feral form, introduced in New Guinea by some of the first human tribes who arrived, and flourishing like the dingo in Australia because it has no competitors except the lowly pouched animals, which are no match for it.

The domestic pig of China, where pigs have been bred for thousands of years, was evidently derived from the East Indian pig. Chinese pigs were imported into Europe and America in the last century, and the crosses between them and the European breeds have produced some of the most valued modern high bred types. The masked pig is the most remarkable of the Chinese breeds. Its skin tends to be loose, and hangs in thick folds on the face as well as on the body, and it has enormous drooping ears. This race produces exceptionally large litters of young, but attempts to cross it with the European breeds seem to have failed.

Everyone has heard of the "Poland China" breed, whose name suggests an origin from the crossing of Asiatic and European swine. This breed, however, seems to have originated entirely in the United States. None of its ancestry can be traced either to Polish or to Chinese blood.

There are a number of wild types of pig-like animals which clearly belong to the pig group, but none of which have been domesticated. We may mention the brightly colored forest pigs of Africa, which are found in the tropical forest. The huge wart hog of the African plains is so hideous with its great knobby head and tremendous tusks that it is a fascinating sight. It was amusing to make the acquaintance of a big boar wart hog in the London Zoo, who liked nothing better than to have his head scratched, and was always hoping for food (and not in vain) when we visited his pen. The

American pigs, known as peccaries, are quite distinct from any of the pigs of the Old World. Their complicated stomach, almost approaching that of the cud-chewing cattle and sheep, is the most surprising difference between them and the common swine. Partly because of their vicious temperament, there seems to have been no attempt to domesticate them.

Most surprising of all the wild swine is the babirusa of Celebes, whose name means "pig-deer" in Malay, and is derived from the four enormous tusks, which rise straight from the snout before they hook backward, so that they really suggest horns more than they do teeth.

The hippopotamus is the only animal more nearly related to the pigs than to any other group. The large common hippopotamus is found in the rivers and swamps over most of Africa, and there is a dwarf relative confined to West Africa. Both are great favorites in zoological gardens.

WALTER A. WEBER